MW00626137

Let's Fix It!

A magic kit for adults with ADHD

LINDA ROGGLI

Let's Fix It!
Copyright © 2011 by Linda Roggli

All rights reserved. Printed in the United States of America
No part of this book may be reproduced or used in any manner whatsoever
without written permission except in case of brief quotations embedded in
critical articles or reviews. For permission, write the publisher:
Passionate Possibility Press, 137 Heather Ridge Ct. Durham, NC 27712

This publication is designed to offer insight into adult Attention Deficit/
Hyperactivity Disorder (AD/HD) but is not a substitute for medical
and psychological assessment or treatment. Seek professional assistance
when indicated. Scientific information contained herein is as accurate as
possible as of the date of publication.

Published by Passionate Possibility Press
Cover design by Linda Roggli
Illustration by Wendy Sefcik

Library of Congress Cataloging-in-Publication data available on request

ISBN-13 978-0-9786409-2-7
ISBN-10 0-9786409-2-6

> Magic is believing in yourself. If you can do that, you can make anything happen.
> *-Johann Wolfgang von Goethe*

*For Janie, who has a love-hate
relationship with her ADHD*

Contents

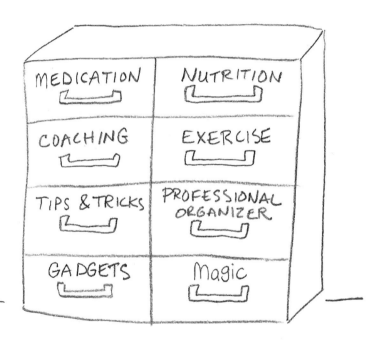

Introduction

More than anything else, when I found out that I had an ADD brain (I use ADD and ADHD interchangeably throughout this book), I wanted to change it, straighten it out, repair it. Isn't that what you are supposed to do with a problem–solve it?

I wanted a magic wand to banish all my previous missteps and replace them with ADD-appropriate solutions that were in harmony with my newly-diagnosed brain. Sadly, I found no such wand.

After years of learning about my brain's ADD-ish-ness, I now know that it "takes a village" of solutions to corral my ADD brain. And while they aren't as alluring as magic, they do wield a certain mystique that sometimes feels other-worldly and clever. And at other times (let's be honest), they feel like drudgery!

The mini-book you hold in your hands–originally written as a bonus chapter for my book about ADD women (*Confessions of an ADDiva: midlife in the non-linear lane*)–is my all-in-one handy-dandy handbook of pseudo-magic for ADD.

As you peruse these pages, know that I have presented the facts as accurately as possible, but the opinions and asides are purely my own–a writer's indulgence with the intention of sharing my personal experience. But my experience is *only* my experience; yours may be different. So, as they say in 12-step programs: take what you like and leave the rest.

And feel free to wave the book around - magic wand-like or use pixie dust when appropriate!

Medication

The big gorilla in the room is medication, which almost all psychiatrists swear is the best treatment for ADD. It is certainly the fastest treatment for ADD. You take a pill (or slap on a patch) and you can focus. Until the medication wears off. But medication also incites heated debate in the ADD community as to safety, effectiveness and potential for abuse.

There are angry accusations that pharmaceutical companies "push" drugs to boost their bottom line. I know enough about corporate America to take those accusations somewhat seriously. But for a lot of folks, ADD meds are quite literally a lifesaver. So here's a look at the lineup of ADD medications. Most of these drugs are

FDA-approved for children only, but doctors routinely prescribe them for grown-ups, too.

There are two kinds of ADD medications: stimulants and non-stimulants. In the stimulant corner are two heavy hitters: amphetamines and methylphenidate (meth-ell-fen'-uh-date). In a strange paradox, stimulants can actually focus even the hyperactive ADD brain by helping our friends Nora Penne Effrin (norepinephrine) and Dope A. Mean (dopamine) effectively bridge the little gap between neurons (also known as the synapse - pronounced like computer applications gone to the dark side, sin-apps).

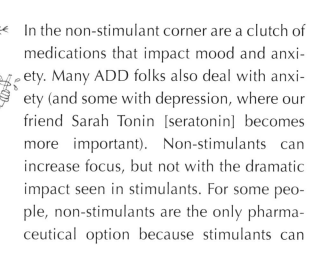

In the non-stimulant corner are a clutch of medications that impact mood and anxiety. Many ADD folks also deal with anxiety (and some with depression, where our friend Sarah Tonin [seratonin] becomes more important). Non-stimulants can increase focus, but not with the dramatic impact seen in stimulants. For some people, non-stimulants are the only pharmaceutical option because stimulants can

Mr. Dope A. Mean

trigger health problems, such as increased heart rate and higher blood pressure.

Although there are many brand names for ADD medications, they belong to only a handful of "families." Sometimes it's hard to keep track of which ones are essentially the same formulation with different delivery systems (the way the medication is released so your body can use it). Let's sort them out to keep the families together; no Hatfield and McCoy family feuds allowed!

Stimulant medication

There are two broad categories of stimulant medication: amphetamines and methylphenidate.

The **Amphetamine** (am-**fett**-a-meen) clan includes:

> **Adderall**®
> **Vyvanse**®
> **Dexedrine**®
> **Dextrostat**®
> **Desoxyn**®

Some of these amphetamines or mixed amphetamine salts are short acting, meaning that their effective cycle is completed in three to five hours. Others have a longer cycle, improving attention and focus for twelve hours or even longer.

The **Methylphenidate** (meth-el-**fen**-ah-date) family includes:
> **Ritalin**®
> **Metadate**®
> **Focalin**®
> **Concerta**®
> **Daytrana**® (patch)

Ritalin was the original stimulant medication approved for treatment of ADHD. It was developed in 1944 and named after the researcher's wife, Rita. It has been much maligned in the press, especially when administered to elementary school children, but it has the longest history of safety. It also has a history of abuse since it can be injected or crushed and snorted.

Drug companies rushed to create new delivery systems to deter abuse. Concerta capsules contain a tiny sponge that slowly expands in the digestive tract, gradually pushing the medication through a pinpoint hole. Daytrana is a thin patch saturated with the medication that is absorbed through the skin and then shuttled to the bloodstream.

The amount and frequency of dosage for stimulants depends not on the weight of the patient, but on the rate that the drug is metabolized (absorbed and utilized) by the body. A petite woman may be prescribed a higher dose of a stimulant than a burly gentleman for both to achieve the same effect on focus and attention.

Non-stimulant medication

There are several non-stimulant ADHD medications:

- **Stratterra**® – atomoxetine (at-o-**mox**-i-teen)
  Atomoxetine is a tricyclic antidepressant formulation that inhibits reuptake of norepinephrine (Yay, Nora!) in the brain. It is used to reduce anxiety rather than to increase focus. It is one of the few medications approved for use by ADHD adults. Dosage is based on body weight.
- **Intuniv**® – guanfacine (**gwan**-fa-seen)
- **Kapvay**® – clonidine (**klon**-a-deen)
  Both guanfacine and clonidine were originally used to treat high blood pressure. They seem to have a

calming effect on ADHD patients and provide some attention and focus improvement. Kapvay has been approved for use alone or as an add-on to stimulant medication.

"Second line" ADHD medication

Some drugs are used "off label" to help ADHD symptoms but are not FDA approved for ADHD treatment. They usually deliver a less robust effect on ADHD symptoms than first line medications. They include:

- **Wellbutrin**® (buproprion), an antidepressant also used in smoking cessation programs
- **Tofranil**® (imipramine), a tricyclic antidepressant that is also used to treat bed wetting
- **Pamelor**® (nortriptyline) also a tricyclic antidepressant
- **Tenex**® (guanfacine), used to treat high blood pressure
- **Catapres**® (clonidine), ditto for blood pressure (both of these meds have an ADHD formulation under a different brand name; *see the previous page.*)

"Controlled substances"

In the United States, ADHD stimulant medications are regulated by the Office of Diversion Control (ODC), an arm of the Drug Enforcement Act (DEA), which is part of the federal Department of Justice. These medications are labeled as "controlled substances," which means they have legitimate medicinal use when taken as prescribed, but there is a high risk of abuse. Stimulants are often bought and sold illegally as street drugs for recreational use.

The DEA ranks controlled substances into five classifications. Amphetamines and methylphenidate are Class II controlled substances. That is useless information unless you also know that Class I drugs include LSD, heroin, peyote and ecstasy; all of them illegal, none of them dispensed for medicinal purposes.

That means Class II drugs are "barely legal." They live at the tippy top of the legal controlled substances pyramid along with powerful pain killers like morphine and oxycodone. The Office of Diversion Control reports Class II drugs have *"a high potential for abuse which may lead to severe psychological or physical dependence."* Some research shows that ADHD stimulants actually deter addiction because the ADHD patient is less prone to use illicit drugs as unwitting self medication.

There are strict requirements for dispensing controlled substances. For instance, to write prescriptions for these drugs a medical professional must hold a current DEA number, which is granted by the federal government.

Pharmacies must have a paper prescription for controlled substances; a phone or fax order will not be accepted. And refills are usually not permitted; however, many US states allow dispensing of a 90-day supply. Of course, this no-refills, paper-prescription rule does not apply to non-stimulant ADD meds like Stratterra® or Intuniv®.

To prevent widespread drug abuse of legal controlled substances, the DEA severely limits production of controlled substances (thus living up to the "control" moniker). These production quotas are based on projected need for the drug and current inventory. The US Attorney General's office makes the quota determination each year. Sometimes, that projection is wrong, as it was in 2010-2011. Many more adults with ADHD were diagnosed than expected, so there were shortages of some stimulant medications.

The FDA maintains a site with information about current shortages and anticipated availability. There is no requirement to report shortages, but most pharmaceutical companies voluntarily comply. The reasons for shortages sometimes have nothing to do with DEA quotas. Sometimes manufacturers experience difficulty in obtaining the active ingredients for ADHD meds (known as the "API" or Active Pharmaceutical Ingredient"). Surprisingly, as much as 40% of the APIs for US drugs are imported from other countries, usually Italy, India or China.

A few words about generic ADHD medications

Some ADD medications are still "under patent" which means that the pharmaceutical company that developed the drug and went through the long process of obtaining FDA approval is allowed to sell it under their brand name. By US law, no one else is permitted to sell that formulation for a period of twelve years; then generic equivalents can be produced.

Not surprisingly, the brand name drug is more expensive than the generic because the drug company must "make hay while the sun shines"–they charge higher prices to offset their research and development expenses. They also reap handsome profits during the years of patent protection. That might sound a bit greedy on the part of Big Pharma, but at least when your doctor prescribes the brand name drug, you know what you are getting.

When you take a generic, the formulation is not *identical* to the proprietary recipe originally developed. It uses an *equivalent* formula. According to FDA regulations, a generic drug may contain as little as 80% of the active ingredient(s) or as much as 125%. My guess is that very few generics contain more than 100% of the active ingredients. Most generics fall within a 4% range either way, which is roughly the same range between batches of brand name drugs. If you are sensitive to medication, however, that small difference can have a big impact on your response to the medication. Some ADD adults sim-

ply must take brand name medication for that reason. Others fare better using generics.

There is yet another significant difference between generics and brand name drugs. A brand name drug consistently manufactures its medication using the same "base"–the filler, the outside coating, etc. And though generic drug companies are held to exacting standards for the active ingredients in medication, they are free to use alternative base ingredients.

I've talked to women who report that their response to generic ADD medication changed when their pharmacy abruptly switched generic manufacturers (often to obtain a lower wholesale price). There is no notification requirement to customers when these changes occur since generics are considered to be interchangeable.

That simply isn't true for some highly sensitive ADD folks. And some generic drugs have a checkered history. When the generic version of Wellbutrin 300 XR was released, there was an immediate increase in the number of patients who reported suicidal thoughts, a direct result of the change in medication. Those problems have been rectified, but it still makes sense to note possible changes in response between brand name and generic medications.

More and more health insurance companies are balking at paying for brand name medication after a generic becomes available. If brand names medications work better for you than generics, you could wind up paying the entire cost of the prescription out of pocket, even with health car coverage.

Pro and con of ADHD meds–quick overview
Pro: stimulants improve focus quickly; medication is usually covered by health insurance; most meds are readily available through local pharmacies; some studies show medication reduces the incidence of illegal substance abuse. Response to medication can offer insight into what neurotransmitters are most affected (in broad strokes, if we respond well to methylphenidate, there is likely a problem with norepinephrine and/or dopamine; a positive response to amphetamines likely means a dopamine deficiency).

Con: serious side effects in some people; difficult to get the right dose of the right drug or combination of drugs; high rate of "non compliance" which means ADD folks often forget to take or stop taking them; expensive if generic is not available; some stimulant doses must be increased over time to maintain effect; some new studies show amphetamines damage neuron cells and increase long term risk of Parkinson's disease (other studies show amphetamines help Parkinson's–the ultimate paradox and frustration of current research).

Please view this brief overview as the **beginning** of your education about ADHD medications. There are websites and books devoted exclusively to this topic. Remember that there is no perfect ADD medication, so work with your doctor to get the best combination of treatments.

People

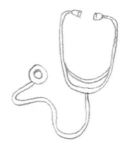

M
ost people think a "Real Doctor," with the initials M.D. after his or her name, is the key to an ADD diagnosis and appropriate treatment. It's true that physicians, especially psychiatrists, do diagnose ADD via functional intake interviews or specialized testing. Some docs use SPECT brain scans although there is still some controversy as to their accuracy for diagnosis. Others use computer testing. And physicians are authorized to write prescriptions for ADHD medications.

But psychologists, nurse practitioners (NPs) and physicians' assistants (PAs) and osteopaths (DOs) can also diagnose ADD, so don't feel that you are limited to medical docs if you're looking for an opinion that will stand up to insurance scrutiny.

Depending on your location, finding a great ADD doc can be simple or excruciatingly difficult. If you live in an area with a "deficit" of ADD professionals, don't despair. You can be tested for ADHD anywhere, then return to your local professionals for treatment and follow-up.

[An aside: most diagnostic testing is not covered by health insurance so be prepared to pay out of pocket. Costs vary widely but a midrange is $400 - $500. Subsequent appointments for medication management and check-ins are usually covered as regular psychiatric or medical care.]

You'll find ADD expertise in some unexpected places. Because they deal with children's ADD, pediatricians can be a good source of information and they may be willing to treat your ADD or at least offer a referral.

As a reminder, in the United States only a physician (MD), osteopath (DO), nurse practitioner (NP) or physician's assistant (PA) can write prescriptions for medication dispensed through a pharmacy.

Beware! Not all MDs, DOs, nurse practitioners, physician assistants and psychologists are created equal in the ADD world. It's not enough to have a license on the wall. Your ADD professional needs ADD-specific training and continuing medical education. They should be aware of (and even better, active in) organizations that support ADHD adults, such as CHADD (Children and Adults with ADHD) or ADDA (Attention Deficit Disorder Association). Don't be intimidated; ask questions. If you can find a local support group, ask for a personal recommendation. It can make all the difference.

Psychologists, therapists and counselors

Psychologists, psychotherapists, social workers and counselors get lumped together, sometimes to their dismay. But their common connection is that they are usually eligible to submit insurance claims for their services, which is great news for ADHD adults who have insurance that covers mental health.

Psychologists (those whose credentials include a doctorate like a Ph.D. or Psy. D.) can diagnose ADD. Some of them use a computer model (often the T.O.V.A. - Test Of Variable Attention); others use a collection of psychological evaluations. Some use lengthy intake interviews, which are quite accurate for diagnosis, as I learned firsthand. Psychologists cannot prescribe medication but often work closely with MDs, NPs or PAs who write scripts for stimulants and other medications.

Psychotherapists (therapists or counselors) hold masters' degrees in psychology or a related field. They usually offer traditional talk therapy, which is an excellent choice for the sidecar problems that almost always accompany ADD: family and relationship issues, depression, mood swings. Talk therapy has not proven effective to improve ADD concentration or focus, however.

Some psychology professionals specialize in Cognitive Behavioral Therapy (CBT), which has been either very effective for ADD or not-so-effective for ADD, depending on which research you choose to read and trust. CBT is behavior modification: teach skills, set expectations and implement consequences.

Coaching, which has its roots in CBT, has a good track record for dealing with the accountability issues which plague ADD. Some psychology professionals have embraced a more coach-like approach to therapy. Since therapy may be reimbursed by insurance, a therapist-coach can be a two-for-one, if that appeals to you.

ADHD coaches

Until recently, there were only a few hundred ADD coaches in the world, but thanks to a growing train-ing sector and heightened interest in coaching, there's probably a coach in your area. While therapists and counselors must meet their clients face-to-face, coach-ing can be done long distance by phone, email and online video conferencing. Most coaches have clients all over the world.

I've heard coaching described as "therapy light," but that's a misnomer. Coaches do work one-on-one with clients like therapists or psychologists, but they focus on accountability and encouragement instead of the reasons behind your behaviors and thoughts. Like an athletic coach, an ADD coach can help you improve your "game" by clarifying your goals and asking the right questions to help you achieve them.

The good news is that ADHD coaching is a short term proposition, usually three to nine months. The bad news is that coaching is not covered by health insurance (although that could be good news if you'd like to maintain your ADD privacy). Expect to pay $50 to $300 or more per session, depending on the coach's experience, location and services offered.

A good ADD coach is worth his or her weight in ADD gold. He or she can be your cheerleader, your educator, your accountability partner, your inspiration. A poor ADD coach (or therapist or psychologist or doctor) can be a disaster. ADD specialization requires specific skills and training.

Coaching is not regulated by state licensure, which opens the door to charlatans. The only way to make sure your ADD coach is legit is to check their training and/or certification. There are now certifications specific to ADHD coaching. It is well worth your time to investigate a prospective coach. *(Download "13 Questions You MUST Ask Your ADHD Coach" on the ADDiva website: http://addiva.net/coaching or under the "Coaching" tab)*.

Many ADD coaches, doctors and other ADD professionals are adults diagnosed with ADD. I am asked often how a professional can be effective when he or she has ADD. I believe that coaches and other professionals who have ADD brains have a more empathetic approach (they *do* understand what you're going through). And professionally-trained coaches, therapists and psychologists are trained to put their own issues aside to focus on *you*.

Team ADDiva
There was a point in the not-too-distant past when I was in constant overwhelm. Everything was falling apart. In desperation I took out a pen and paper and wrote down everything I was doing (or should be doing). It was a long list and contained far more things than I could

ever accomplish in my waking hours: laundry, gardening, feeding the dogs, snuggling with Victor, editing my website, coaching my clients, going to the gym, replacing light bulbs, hanging pictures and dozens more.

Then I went through the list and checked off the tasks that could be (and should be) accomplished *only* by me. No one else could write my books, facilitate my retreats or snuggle with Victor (of course not!). No one else could organize my office or plan my garden. Those tasks required my special touch; they were my avenues to share my gifts with the world.

As I reviewed the list once again, I realized that there were some things I had always done that did *not* require my personal touch. I did not have to be the person who checked the post office box every day. I'm not the only one who could weed the vegetable garden or fix dinner for my (much adored) dogs.

It was hard to let go of my ownership of those tasks, to admit to myself that I wasn't superwoman. But gradually, I loosened my grip on many of those "I have to do it" tasks.

I began to systematically outsource the jobs that didn't require my personal attention. That's when Team ADDiva began to take shape.

I found a kiddo in the neighborhood who would pull weeds for $8.00 an hour. My time is worth more than that and the guilt it relieved was priceless. Of course, I had to spend a couple of hours showing him the difference between a weed and a seedling and he made some mistakes but that was OK.

Now, I could have hired this kiddo to *plant* my garden, but that's the part of gardening I love. It feeds me, fills me with creativity and anticipation. So that's a job I will never outsource; I am quite selective about this.

Before you protest that you can't afford to "outsource" cleaning your toilets or weeding the flower bed, know that this plan doesn't have

Out, out, darned weed!

to cost a lot of money. "Outsourcing" can start with your own family members.

For instance, if you are doing the laundry for everyone in your household, stop it right now! Unless you love to wash clothes, laundry does not require your personal touch. Show the non-laundry-aware members of your family how to operate the washer and dryer and let them loose.

Be resolute about your commitment to yourself; don't give in and throw in a couple of loads when they run out of clean clothes. They can throw in a couple of loads just as easily as you can. The same technique also applies to starting dinner or mowing the lawn. And friends or neighbors can be outsource partners, too, especially if you work out a bartering system to share the load.

Over the years, I have had the pleasure of working with a variety of ADDiva team members. I don't use them all at once–that would be too expensive! But I make use of them when I truly need them. **Don't skip this section just**

because money is involved - you may find inspiration for your own ADD here.

Professional organizers

A lot of people refuse to consider hiring a professional organizer because they think they need to banish their piles first (kind of like cleaning your house before the cleaning lady comes). That's just silly, although I experienced the same reluctance.

There's a lot of embarrassment about being unable to do the basics like keep your own space clean and tidy. However, no matter what kind of shape your house or apartment is in, professional organizers have seen worse–dog poop in the dining room, maggots in closets. Don't worry about it. Just call them (if you can find that elusive slip of paper with their phone number!).

Professional organizers were once scarce commodities. Now, thanks to television shows about hoarders and clean

The piles get neater
with a professional organizer

houses, they are popping up everywhere. There is certification for professional organizers but not everyone who claims to be an organizer has taken classes. Quality is a bit uneven, so look for someone who has been in the business for more than a few months. Most importantly, you want someone who is non-judgmental and willing to adapt to your style.

Professional organizers work by the hour, usually in three-to-four hour blocks. Prices range from $45 - $150 or more an hour. How many sessions will it take to get "done?" That depends on how much clutter you've accumulated and how far down the decluttering road you want to go.

If you can stand to part with some of your stuff, it will be a lot easier (and cheaper) to go through some of the mess before you meet with the organizer. But sometimes we need a professional to get us started. Remember, ADD means problems with initiating tasks as well as completing them so it may take a professional to help sort out the good, the Goodwill and the good-for-nothing.

Don't overlook the possibility of help from a good friend if a professional is out of your budget. Just make sure they are coming in to sort, not to judge. Or you may need a body double, someone to merely sit with you while you work.

Body Double
The name is misleading; a Body Double doesn't mirror your activities. They simply are a presence in the space, which for some odd reason, helps us to focus.

My husband Victor acted as a Body Double when he came to my office while I reorganized the file cabinets. Note that he didn't *do* anything except sit there. We didn't even speak to each other; I needed to focus all my attention on the task at hand. He read his medical journals; I worked.

A Body Double must be someone willing to be in the room and **give no advice.** They are not allowed to judge your mess or project or progress. Their energy is what you need; not their counsel. Be careful about this if you invite a family member or good friend to act as your Body Double. They may have long experience with you and have some established opinions about how you should proceed. Sometimes, a new acquaintance can be a better Body Double than an old friend.

If you use a Body Double, do *not* entertain them. They are not your guest; they are a silent partner. Not only silent, but immobile, at least for me. Having someone walk around is a distraction I don't need. Get them a cup of tea and let them knit or write or read. No phone calls–overhearing their conversation could pull you off course.

Housekeeper/cleaning person/straightener-upper
Even if you live in a tiny studio apartment, your ADD can slowly (or not so slowly) create piles and laundry and

dust that sit there, leering at you day after day. They will drive you crazy. So hire a housekeeper once in a while. Or regularly.

When my sons were toddlers, my mother gifted me with a once-a month cleaning lady named Hoselena. I am not making this up; that was really her name. It was the best gift ever: clean bathrooms gave me a small dose of sanity.

I have ADD clients who use a cleaning service only when the dirt gets out of control and others who have someone come in twice a week. If you can't afford any extra expense, invite a friend over to help you clean (like a Body Double who works with you) and then reciprocate by heading over to his or her house. There's no cost to either of you except time.

Where's Mary Poppins when we need her?

Training household help can be a challenge for ADD folks. More than once, I've fallen into Little Red Hen mode - "I'll just do it myself!" But it's worth the time to teach someone that they are to wipe off the counters and to leave your piles untouched.

Handyman

There is always stuff to fix around my house–broken lamps, closet shelves that have fallen down, chipped paint in the hallway. I know how to fix a lot of those things, but do I fix them? Nope. They sit there for years waiting for me to get around to them. I think it might be a small bit of procrastination.

Something always needs fixing

So when I finally found a reliable handyman ($25-$60 an hour) it was like lifting a veil from my life. My guilt about not hanging the picture or fixing the light had dragged me down more than I realized. In just a few hours (far less time than it would have taken me) I felt like a free woman again.

Having someone to call when you're in a crunch lets you focus on what's important: the things only you can do. Of course you don't need a handyman every week or even every month, but he or she is an invaluable part of Team

ADDiva. *[Aside: your husband, wife or partner may be willing to take on this role, but be careful about overloading him or her with a long Honey Do list; it can devastate a relationship.]*

Other members of Team ADDiva

- **Good appliance repair guy or gal** (might be your handyman)
- **Dry cleaner that offers pick up** and delivery at your home or work
- **Laundry service -** drop off in the morning, pick up at night
- **Landscaper** to handle the heavy stuff
- **Bank person who knows your name -** invaluable for overdrafts or credit line expansion
- **Friendly neighbor** who will watch the kids, accept UPS packages and/or trade organizing and Body Double services
- **Sitter for kids or aging parents** so you have some much-needed time off

Alternatives

If you browse the internet looking for ADD cures, there is no lack of potions and supplements that purport to heal and mitigate ADD symptoms. There are testimonials from parents who swear that a particular diet transformed their child from monster to sweetheart. There are pills with mystical ingredients guaranteed to call your neurons to attention. There are mind exercises and balance boards to train the two hemispheres of your brain to work together. There are hands-on healers. There are reading exercises. In other words, there's a lot of room for fraud. There's also room for possibilities!

Nutrition

Right after I found out about my ADD, a therapist I was seeing gave me a diet called the "Pre-frontal Cortex Diet." It was a low carbohydrate diet with lots of protein: eggs and bacon for breakfast, a salad with chicken or fish for lunch and meat and plain veggies for dinner. Pretty bland, with no scientific back-up to prove its effectiveness. Nonetheless, I felt better when I tried it, perhaps because it curtailed carbohydrates, one of my ADD sore spots.

It's easy for me to get on the carbohydrate roller coaster (eat bread, fruit or something sweet, feel great, then crash and crave even more bread, fruit or sweets, repeat 'til comatose with sugar). What I learned over the years is that fewer carbs stabilize my blood sugar, which also keeps my ADD on an even keel. The problem is that my brain really wants carbs, thanks to my party animal friend Dope A. Mean (dopamine). I have to be a strict disciplinarian.

Protein for breakfast, please!

Very restrictive diets like the Feingold plan, established in the 1960s, eliminate food coloring and other synthetic additives from foods ingested. Recently, the FDA investigated the effect of food dyes on children (deliberately feeding them drinks loaded with dye). The results were mixed but there does seem to be a connection between behavior and food dye. The link between ADHD and nutrition is still fuzzy. There is only a smattering of peer-reviewed research about nutrition and the ADHD brain, but it is an area of intense interest. It may well be that diet *does* play an important role in ADD. Stay tuned.

Supplements

The jury is still out on whether nutritional supplements help ADD. There are proponents of supplements who swear they make a difference. It might be a powerful placebo effect. Or perhaps their symptoms of "ADD" were triggered by food allergies or even prescription medication. There is new research that points to histamines as a possible source of inattentive, ADD-like actions in children. Much more research is needed. In the meantime, I'll share my experience with a few supplements.

Fish oil and omega-3 fatty acids

The most compelling evidence to improve brain plasticity and brain function comes from research on fish oil supplements that provide omega-3 fatty acids. Our Western diet is full of omega-6 fatty acids but relatively few omega-3s.

Fish oil is good for your brain

Medline, the US government's website for medical information, credits fish oil for helping lower triglyceride levels, improve health and possibly reduce high blood pressure. There is a long list of other potential positive benefits including alleviating menstrual pain, buffering rheumatoid arthritis and lowering cholesterol.

The original fish oil research about brain function was conducted on children ages 8-14 with learning disabilities (LD). After taking a combination of fish oil and evening primrose oil for several months, the LD kids advanced one full grade level in reading, while the control group progressed at the same grade level. Of course, there is now contradictory research that refutes this claim, but my psychiatrist continues to recommend the use of pharmaceutical grade fish oil.

There appears to be no down side to taking fish oil daily except for an occasional tummy upset. Fish oil does act as a blood thinner (like aspirin) so mention your supplement to the doctor if you must have surgery or dental work.

The optimal amount for ADHD adults each day? Between 2500-3500 mg of combined EPA and DHA. A word about getting the correct amount of omega-3 fatty acids. The total amount of oil proclaimed on the front of the bottle can be misleading. The important numbers are on the BACK of the label–the amount of DHA and EPA. Add those two numbers together to get the amount of omega-3 that you need.

Also, you might want to avoid my mistake: I thought that taking one capsule would give me the amount of EPA and DHA on the back label. I finally reread the label: the "serving size" was TWO capsules to equal 1280 omega-3s. I had been taking only half the amount I needed. Ack!

[An aside about storing fish oil capsules. After you open the package, oil tends to go rancid, so always store the capsules or liquid in the freezer. The oil won't freeze

but stays fresh. This technique also reduces that awful fish "burp" that sometimes accompanies our omega-3 booster.]

"Attention" supplements

I am always skeptical of supplements that don't have some sort of peer-reviewed research to back up their claims. Most companies who manufacture supplements have their own testing and research labs, which is a blatant conflict of interest. *Of course* their tests show excellent results; they want to sell you their supplements! My husband disdainfully calls this "junk science."

Nonetheless, I have tried several vitamin supplements that purport to help increase focus, attention and memory, with varying degrees of success.

"Attend®" is sold by VAXA and is part of their three-pronged homeopathic approach to helping ADD. I did notice a difference in my anxiety level when I took Attend, but not much change in focus. The company claims that results from the computerized TOVA (Test of

Variable Attention) improved when ADD children took Attend. Perhaps it works better for children than adults.

VAXA's other supplements suggested for ADD are "Exstress" to alleviate stress and "Memorin" for memory enhancement. I found no benefit to these supplements. The Memorin, in particular, upset my system a bit, so I stopped using it after only two doses.

I did seem to get a focus response from FocusSmart®, a vitamin and mineral supplement I bought at my local wholesale warehouse. It contained an ingredient that is supposed to increase alertness, which is the effect I noticed. However, FocusFactor®, a far more expensive brand, had no effect. Essentially, it is a cornucopia of vitamins and minerals, which aren't bad, but not particularly helpful for focus.

Victor remains less than enthusiastic about my experimentation. So far, no ill effects have been felt, except in my budget. I heed his opinions, however So *be careful* when you take supplements. The companies who produce them, while well intentioned, are profit centers, not research centers. They want your money. And their combination of "natural" ingredients does not guarantee safety. Some herbal supplements have been shown to have serious health consequences. We're right back to "caveat emptor" (let the buyer beware).

Exercise

The most effective "alternative" non-medication treatment for ADD is (drum roll please) exercise. It not only boosts focus and concentration, but primes the pump for better sleep. It helps midlife waistlines and body tone. It boosts bone density and it lifts depression. It's the perfect non-prescription prescription.

So if exercise is so good for us, why do the majority of ADD adults pledge to go to the gym but consistently miss their yoga class? It's the chicken and egg scenario. We need focus and concentration to stick with exercise. Exercise will give us focus and concentration, but we have to get ourselves focused to exercise: so which comes first? The focus or the exercise? It's a vicious circle.

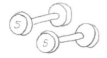

'Round and 'round we go, trying to squeeze in exercise, which absolutely, positively 100% works for our brains while we continue to procrastinate.

Exercise is one of those "just do it" things that probably deserves a kick in the pants to push the circle into reverse order. We are focused, so we make it to exercise class which makes us more focused. Upward spiral!

Memory training
There are a lot of brain exercises out there but none are as well-researched and supported by the scientific community as the one developed in Sweden that trains working memory. Working memory, which you may (or may not) recall, is crucial to executive function. The original psychologists who developed the computer program were trying to help children with learning disabilities, but the program turns out to have a positive effect on ADD, memory issues due to aging and other brain glitches.

In keeping with my pledge to mention only treatments with which I had personal experience, I am embarrassed to tell you that I was a working memory training dropout.

The first time I tried the training, I honestly didn't have the time to devote to the intense regimen. And I found that I disliked the program because it uses computer challenges similar to video games. I abhor video games.

However, I stuck with it the second time and finished the program, boosting my working memory by several percentage points. Not a top notch result, but respectable. The program plays to my weaknesses, which, of course, is the point. Easy exercises wouldn't push my brain into better function. So even though I don't like it, I view working memory training like taking vitamins and eating liver: a necessary evil.

The program I used is administered only by medical doctors and psychologists. My provider (a psychiatrist) found that the program works quite well for children. The program itself was less effective for adults, probably because we have a lifetime of creating strategies that circumvent our ADD.

Even with better working memory skills, we first must unlearn the bad old strategies and relearn new and improved ones. That takes time and effort. My psychia-trist formed a post-training support group to help adult graduates implement changes into their lives. And she recommends strongly that adults continue the follow-up program even after completing the original training.

The price of this program is high–from $1500 to $1800 for the five week course. But the program might be worth it. After all, the price of ADD is pretty high, too.

Meditation

It seems ludicrous to ask a fidgety ADD adult to sit still long enough to contemplate his or her navel. Well, OK, meditation isn't really about your belly button, but it does require some concentration and single-mindedness that runs contrary to the ADD brain's natural bent.

Perhaps that's why it has been shown to work excep-tionally well in calming the ADD brain. Like working memory training, it plays to our weaknesses. Similarly, with practice, we improve our "scores" and meditation becomes easier and more effective.

A 2007 study released by the University of California indicated positive response for adults and adolescents with ADD when they completed an eight-week mindfulness meditation course. The researchers called for even more studies, but the evidence seems clear that there is cognitive improvement as well as reduced anxiety and depression.

My experience with meditation is hit or miss, probably like many of my ADD brethren. I do feel better when I allow my mind to quiet (even when I have to call it back 100 times during a 30 minute session). Eventually, my breathing slows and my attention settles down. Although I don't meditate regularly, I find that when I return to it, my focus more quickly finds a place of rest and restoration. Like body memory, perhaps my brain experiences "meditation memory."

Other honorable mentions
Neurofeedback has its place in ADD treatment, especially for children. I have worked with neurofeedback only briefly and can see the potential benefits. Research results are inconclusive at the moment but that is unimportant if it helps you. A woman in our support group

reported great results at first, then as time went on, she slipped back into her ADD-ish patterns.

I am quite interested in **music therapy** that is tuned to particular wave patterns in our brains. I have not figured out whether we need more theta and less beta and I'm sure there are proponents on both sides of the argument. The ADD sound therapy I have used has not made much of an impact on my concentration, despite claims to the contrary. But if it works for you, three cheers!

There are a number of additional alternative treatments for ADD not mentioned here because I have not personally tested them. The world is full of opportunities to assist ADD; find the solutions that work in your life.

Gadgets

I am a gadget kind of gal, which isn't surprising since my ADD loves anything new and complex. I could spend hours waxing poetic about iPhone apps and bluetooth headsets. I will try to restrain myself and offer only a light dusting of my favorites.

Wireless phone headsets

Nothing rocked my world quite as much as the wireless headset I use for my office phone. I bought my first one for coaching. Since most coaches work by phone, a headset frees our hands to take notes. I soon realized the value of being able to walk around while talking on the phone (multi-tasking, here I come!). I can work in the garden while I talk. I can pace back and forth to release my anxiety. I can do dishes. I can even go to the bath-room while I am listening to teleclasses (don't tell any-one; I only go there when I'm "muted!").

I adore my wireless headset so much so that I bought one for my house. Then I bought one for GardenSpirit, my retreat house. Then I bought one for my bedroom. For me, they are essential to managing my ADD. My current favorite: *GN Netcom 9125 (now produced by Jabra).*

By contrast, the bluetooth headset for my cell phone was awful. It would fall off my ear, I would accidentally dis-connect calls when I was trying to increase the volume, and the sound was atrocious. I finally found the equiv-alent of my wonderful wireless headset in cell phone form. It's the one used by long distance truckers and has crystal clear reception and transmission. Freedom at last! Hands-down favorite: *Blue Parrot 250-XT.*

FOFA
Clients and ADD folks ask one question more than any other: "How can I keep track of my car keys?" My answer is always the same: FOFA - short for Find One,

Find All®. These ingenious key finders have little beepers embedded in keychains with number pads on the surface. I attach one to my keys, another to my purse (on the strap), another to my camera. When I want to find my keys, I can push the FOFA on my purse and it rings the keys! Amazing! If I can find one of those three FOFAs, I can ring any of the others. Problem solved.

Smart pen

I have hankered for something that would allow me to take notes and record sound at the same time. A few years ago, someone finally invented it: the Smart Pen. In a barrel that looks a lot like a fountain pen is a tiny camera that captures my handwriting (ugh!) as well as a microphone (yay!). Everything is saved and transferred to my computer via USB. Wow. This is one of life's minor miracles in my humble opinion. Prices have dropped dramatically and quality has improved so it's a no brainer for ADD. Current favorite: *Echo pen by Livescribe.*

Atomic clocks

I have gradually replaced almost all the clocks in my house and office with atomic versions. I never have to set them. They change automatically when we "fall back" or "spring ahead" during seasonable time changes. And even when I need to replace the batteries, they reset themselves again within minutes. Thank you, atomic clock inventors. You are helping me get to appointments on time. Usually.

iPhone/smart phone

I won't go on and on about how my iPhone helps my ADD, but let's just say that I now have my calendar synced from my office, my appointments are always within reach, I can get my email on the road and I can set alarms so I start and stop projects more easily. The voice recognition software is an ADHD miracle in a phone. Enough said. Isn't there an app for that?

Ditto for my iPad, which I also adore. I can work anywhere and the iPad keypad is *so* much easier for my 50-something eyes and fingers.

Labeler

I suppose I should have listed my P-Touch Brother labeler first in this list. It is certainly first in my heart. I label almost everything: files, cabinet drawers, headset, copier directions, location of mobile phones (on the back of the phone), notebooks, makeup bottles, tires with PSI limits, electrical circuit box, garden tools, sinks, storage containers, transformers for computer accessories, nail polish containers, shoe boxes, clothes hampers ... more every day. I tell Victor that if he stands still too long, I might even label him!

A note about labels: yes, masking tape works too, but only if you can read your handwriting. My dysgraphia precludes that solution. Also, masking tape is not laminated; the label tapes are. The labeler itself is relatively inexpensive. You can find older models in discount sites or on ebay. The laminated tapes are not inexpensive. Order them in bulk from a discount store or the internet.

Timers

Normally I am unenthused about nagging reminders like timers, but they do work for me sometimes. I like unusual sounds, though, so I am not annoyed by the darned things. My favorite is a Tibetan bowl timer that was designed to be used as a telephone ringer. The bowl timer is easy to set (a knob, not buttons), has a big bright display and rings loudly the first time. Then it divides the original time in half and rings again. The timer goes off more and more frequently until it is chiming every two seconds. By that time, I am irritated or resigned to turning the alarm off. And at least I stop (or start) the next project.

The world of gadgets constantly shifts, expands and contracts (which is the reason I love it; not a dull or boring moment in sight). There will be more can't-live-without-it ADHD "stuff" on the horizon. Perhaps a A Star Trek-like transporter that whisks me to my appointments instead of simply reminding me? Or a computer that doesn't crash? Ah, bring on that magic wand! In the meantime, check the ADDiva website for updates. *http://addiva.net/linda-recommends*

Tips & Tricks

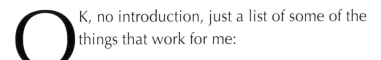

Ok, no introduction, just a list of some of the things that work for me:

1. Several clocks in every room (especially the bathroom) so I can track time more easily.

2. Duplicate bottles of medication in the places I frequent most often - in the car, purse, bathroom, kitchen, office, retreat house (it takes two).

3. SuperSticky PostIts that stick to almost everything - for computer, car, mirrors (only ONE item written on each one).

4. Spiral notebooks for notes and phone messages so I don't lose the pages. (Wide rule works better for my handwriting - lots of white space).

5. Three-ring notebooks for every class, every committee, every client, every project, (2") large enough to hold spiral notebooks and a set of plastic dividers.

6. A dozen pairs of cheap readers (glasses) with "strings" on them so they don't fall off. I never lose the cheapies; only my prescription glasses get lost!

7. Foam drink holders rimmed with feathers that are located on every desk to hold my reading glasses (I can always find them - look for the feathers!).

8. Multiple clothes hampers because I hate to sort dirty clothes (one for underwear, blacks, bras, colors, jeans).

9. Colorful file folders that are coded. (I have a color key posted on each cabinet so everyone knows purple folders are ADDiva, red folders are expenses, etc.).

10. Grouping clothes in the closet by color - makes them easy to find and coordinate.

11. Turning piles into files. Even if it's a pile of files, there is at least some order. I use SuperSticky PostIts® to identify the contents of the files so I don't have to go through them again — remember to THINK ONCE).

12. Bookmarking the things I want to buy online but holding out on making the actual purchases. I can come back later to buy the item (if I remember). This helps curb impulsivity and saves money in the long run.

13. Measuring first before buying organizing supplies, no matter how tempting and neat-nik-inspiring they are.

14. Purging stuff that frustrates me - dull knives, fussy clothes, shoes that pinch, broken canister I'll never fix - less stuff means less organizing.

15. Arranging small adjustable tables ($20 each) in a circle around me to sort big messes. I can move the tables to another room, then come back to the sorting; no one "messes" with my mess.

16. Regularly patrolling my closet for rejects and little-worn clothing. One year I got rid of 70% of my winter clothes (really scary at the time) but found that I didn't miss them at all even after I donated them to charity. And I felt light. And free.

17. Getting outside every morning and take a walk. It stimulates the melatonin in my brain so I can wake up to the day (rain or shine). Turns on my serotonin, too (yay, Ms. Tonin).

18. Duplicate sets of makeup in my purse, bathroom, car and travel kit so I never end up without mascara 10 minutes before I am supposed to give a graduation speech (yes, it really happened).

19. Reconnect to the earth. I love to plant new seedlings. I walk slowly under newly-leafed-out trees. I run my

fingers through the grass. I breathe deeply and remember Who I Really Am (which I forget regularly). Oh yeah, I *am* a magnificent woman!

20. Taking Five Minutes to Put It Away. I *do* have enough time to do it. (This is the most difficult one for me to remember.)

21. Creating a permanent grocery list. I rambled through the kitchen cabinets, freezer and refrigerator and made a list of my most-replaced food items. Then I typed them into the computer and added checkboxes. I even ordered the list to correspond to the layout of my favorite grocery store. Now I just print lots of copies and post one on the refrigerator each week. When I run out of something, I simply check off that item and then try to remember to take the list with me when I go shopping!

And there's more…

If any of these tips, tricks, professionals, medications, supplements, etc. improve your ADD, congratulations! You may have decided that you have finally "fixed it."

Trust me, it's only temporary. ADD isn't something that responds well to the quick fix. Each of these "tricks" is a finger in the dike. They may stave off the flood, but they cannot repair the dam. A combination of them can create a web of plugs that can keep the flood at bay most of the time.

To be truly at peace with ADD requires a closer look at the person behind the ADD brain. *You.* So gather all the "solutions" that work for you, then take a step back to see Who You Really Are inside that web. Make sure you maintain your integrity and authenticity. Then live your life out loud as the glorious ADD adult you were born to be!

Resources

H ere's where you can find some of the items mentioned in these pages. And where to find a smattering of the research info, too.

Brother P-touch labelers
http://www.brother-usa.com/ptouch/

Tibetan bell timer
http://www.now-zen.com/Phone_Bell.html

Atomic clocks
http://www.everyatomicclock.com/All-Atomic-Clocks-C117852.html

Smart pen
http://www.livescribe.com/en-us/smartpen/

Find One Find All key finder
http://www.findonefindall.com/

iPhone and iPad
http://apple.com

Cogmed memory training
http://cogmed.com

ADHD coaches professional organization
http://adhdcoaches.org

Bluetooth headset for cell phone
http://www.vxicorp.com/products/blueparrott-
bluetooth-mobile-solutions/bluetooth-headsets/
b250-xt/

Wireless headset for land lines/USB
http://www.jabra.com/NA-US/headsetsolutions/Pages/
JabraGN9100.aspx

National Organization of Professional Organizers
http://napo.net

Professional Organizers in Canada
http://organizersincanada.com

Handyman & house cleaners
http://craigslist.com

Brain supplement reviews
(as close to unbiased as I could find online)
http://brainresearchsupplements.com/

Exercise videos
http://www.collagevideo.com/

Nutrition and exercise community (free)
http://sparkpeople.com

Reference and further reading

Ritalin/methylphenidate
http://www.cesar.umd.edu/cesar/drugs/ritalin.asp

Amphetamines
http://www.cesar.umd.edu/cesar/drugs/amphetamines.asp

Guanfacine
http://www.ncbi.nlm.nih.gov/pubmedhealth/
PMH0000057/

Atomoxetine/Stratterra
http://www.ncbi.nlm.nih.gov/pubmedhealth/
PMH0000222/

FDA Drug Shortages
http://www.fda.gov/Drugs/DrugSafety/DrugShortages/
ucm050792.htm

Fish oil research
http://www.nlm.nih.gov/medlineplus/druginfo/natu-
ral/993.html

Excellent scholarly articles about ADHD can be found in
the "Journal of Attention Disorders," published by Sage
Publications online at: http://jad.sagepub.com

More information is found on the ADDiva website:
http://addiva.net

About us

Linda Roggli, PCC, is a professional certified coach and the founder of the ADDiva Network, a whimsical and supportive connection for midlife women with ADD-ish tendencies. She is the author of *Confessions of an ADDiva: midlife in the non-linear lane* (2011), *Durham: Doorway to Discovery* (1995) and *Angie's Choice* (2005).

She organizes and moderates a 600-member AD/HD adult support group that meets twice monthly in central NC. She is vice president of the board for ADDA (Attention Deficit Disorder Association) and has moderated its webinar series since 2006. She is a popular presenter at national AD/HD conferences and is a contributor to and guest blogger for *ADDitude* magazine.

GardenSpirit, Linda's women's garden retreat center, is located on eight acres in suburban Durham, NC and includes a 60-foot outdoor labyrinth, purple tree house and meditation paths.

Linda trained as a spiritual life coach before stepping into AD/HD coaching in 2005; she now holds certification from the International Coach Federation and Coach for Life.

In her spare time, Linda teaches organic gardening and plays with her three adorable Shelties and one fabulous husband who often co-facilitates her AD/HD couples' retreats.

Visit her at www.addiva.net.

Wendy Lynn Sefcik is an illustrator/designer/author, owner of Broken Box Designs, LLC (a custom illustration & design studio). She's addicted to artsy things and obsessed with color!

She is a Summa Cum Laude honor graduate of The University of Akron with a Bachelors Degree in Fine & Applied Arts. Wendy lives in Northeastern, Ohio with her family.

For more information visit www.BrokenBoxDesigns.com.

Share your own Tips & Tricks

Sign up for the ADDiva Network to share your
favorite ADHD tips and tricks

http://addivanetwork.com

With every trick or tip you submit, you increase your
chances of winning an
autographed copy of Linda's acclaimed book:

Confessions of an ADDiva: midlife in the non-linear lane

(this QR code takes you directly
to the Tips & Tricks section;
just scan it with your phone camera after
you download a QR reader app)

"I've stopped apologizing to doorknobs..."

http://confessionsofanaddiva.com

"A page turner! Captivating! Validating!
Honest and humorous!"
—Nancy Ratey, M.Ed. SCAC,
author of *The Disorganized Mind*

Get your copy of
"Confessions of an ADDiva- midlife in the non-linear lane"
on Amazon.com (also available as Kindle book
or on the Barnes and Noble color Nook)
Audio book available from the confessions website:

http://confessionsofanaddiva.com

This page intentionally left blank because, um, you're ADD and you'll want to jot down a few notes, right?